My Friend

My friend
likes to eat pizza
with me.

My friend
likes to read books
with me.

We put the food in the car.

Rain

The zoo

My friend
likes to ride bikes
with me.

My friend
likes to jump rope
with me.

My friend
likes to bake cookies
with me.

My friend
likes to play ball
with me.

My friend
likes to do puzzles
with me.

THE UNITED STATES OF AMERICA

15

I like my friend.

My friend likes me.